KATE PUR
with LEE EPTING & JOSH

THE
WORKBOOK

COMPOSURE

THE ART OF EXECUTIVE PRESENCE

Published in the United States by
Surrogate Press®
an imprint of Faceted Press®

Surrogate Press, LLC

Park City, Utah

SurrogatePress.com

ISBN: 978-1-947459-61-8

Book cover and interior design by:

Ali Wright, DAPPER FOX DESIGN

TABLE OF
CONTENTS

CHAPTER 1
THE HIGH ACHIEVER

——————

THE HIGH ACHIEVER

KEY TAKEAWAYS

✓ Our past history often contributes to present struggles and areas where we feel stuck.

✓ Self Determination Theory explains the motivational pattern, common for high performers, that creates an overemphasis on external validation that high performers experience.

> ▷ Extrinsic (external) motivation patterns involve seeking rewards from external factors, such as grades, accomplishments, titles, evaluations, and the opinions of others.
>
> > ▸ Those who are primarily externally motivated are extraordinarily adept at accomplishing things that garner approval and acknowledgement, they rarely fail, and avoid trying new things to sidestep failure.
> >
> > ▸ Those who are primarily externally motivated are extremely sensitive to judgement, criticism, and failure; when they experience these they react with self-blame, guilt, and shame. What would be perceived as a minor setback for most becomes devastating for these high performers.
>
> ▷ In contrast Intrinsic (internal) motivation patterns involve being motivated more from within, by interests, curiosity, passions, and their own intrinsic values.
>
> > ▸ Those who are primarily internally motivated are willing to try anything, even at the risk of mistakes and failure, but don't experience self-doubt, shame, or guilt, if they should happen to fail.
> >
> > ▸ Those who are primarily internally motivated rarely cave to societal pressures, nor are they motivated by money, prestige, and accolades.

✓ We refer to any in the minority as being in the out group. In its simplest terms, an individual is part of an out group if they do not identify with the dominant demographic of a workplace.

WRITING EXERCISE

1. Are there any areas in your work or personal life that you feel stuck?

_____

_____

_____

_____

_____

_____

2. List several key challenges or traumatic situations you faced in your past.

_____

_____

_____

_____

_____

_____

3. List several key successes or personal accomplishments from your past.

_____

_____

_____

_____

_____

_____

4. What are the biggest challenges you face in your work life?

_____

_____

_____

_____

_____

_____

_____

5. On the following continuum, mark the place where you think your motivation lies
   between externally and internally motivated:

O—O—O—O—O—O—O—O—O—O

INTERNAL   EXTERNAL

6. In what areas of your life are you internally motivated? How do you know?

_____

_____

_____

_____

_____

_____

7. In what areas of your life are you externally motivated? How do you know?

_____

_____

_____

_____

_____

_____

CHAPTER 2

THE IMPOSTER SYNDROME

———

KEY TAKEAWAYS

Impostor Syndrome

1. Our definition of **Impostor Syndrome**: when an individual perceives their competence to be less than others perceive it to be, despite evident success.

2. 75% of female executives report experiencing Impostor Syndrome at certain points in their careers.

   ▷ 81% of women put more pressure on themselves to not fail than men do

   ▷ 56% report being afraid they won't live up to expectations

   ▷ 47% say their feelings of self-doubt are because they never expected to reach such a high level of success

   ▷ 32% of women who identify with Impostor Syndrome didn't know there were others like them

Impostor Behaviors

The five "fingerprint" Impostor Syndrome behaviors, and how they show up in people:

1. **Lack of Confidence** - While generally quite confident, certain situations create anticipatory anxiety and self-doubt. This lack of confidence can be paralyzing especially if they are faced with taking on something new, or handling a role or project that tests the limits of their skill and experience. Their self-doubt often impedes the kind of experimentation and trial-and-error that leads to faster learning and growth.

2. **Rejection Sensitivity** - Sensitivity to being judged, criticized, or found lacking. They tend to personalize the reactions of others, internalizing any type of criticism and feedback. When they feel judged, instead of learning from it, they are likely to experience shame. Many experience constant people-pleasing and approval-seeking, which is exhausting.

3. **Depressed Entitlement** - The feeling of being part of the "out group" with a persistent fear that they don't measure up to their colleagues. They constantly feel the need to work harder than others in order to prove themselves. They judge themselves too harshly, often undervalue their contributions, and may feel less deserving of their title and compensation.

4. **Perfectionism** - Striving for flawlessness that drives them to over-prepare and over-work, often with wasted effort that hardly ever leads to a commensurate payoff. Impostors rarely experience the satisfaction of accomplishment. They unwittingly perpetuate the cycle of anxiety, overwork, and fleeting sense of accomplishment followed immediately by the anxiety of the next looming task— which starts the cycle anew.

5. **Feeling like a Fraud** - They never really feel like they have achieved true success, leaving them feeling as though they don't deserve the rewards of status, prestige or money that result. Instead, they feel inauthentic and phony. They fear being exposed as a fraud, that people will find out that *it's all a lie*.

    ▷ Entry-level employees and first-level managers tend to score higher in their Impostor Behaviors.

    ▷ Women tend to score higher in lack of confidence, depressed entitlement, and rejection sensitivity.

    ▷ Impostor Behaviors often remain dormant when things are going well but flare up in high pressure situations.

The Brain Hack:

1. Imagine a situation in which you might experience Impostor Behaviors.

2. Imagine a clone is sitting next to you who is identical to you in every way—has the same life experiences, the same education and experience, the same pressures and dynamics in their personal life.

3. Imagine that the clone never experiences the fear, self-doubt and anxiety associated with your Impostor Behaviors.

4. Now imagine your clone in the situation in question #1. "Test drive" this clone version of yourself to understand how your life might be different without an Impostor Behavior.

I Can't Do This Because _____ I Could Do This If _____

1. Imagine something you'd like to do but are reluctant or afraid.

2. Instead of saying to yourself "I can't do that because," say "I can do that if" and list the conditions under which you *could* do it successfully.

THE IMPOSTOR SYNDROME
WRITING EXERCISE

1. **Visit composurethebook.com/assessment to take the Impostor Breakthrough Assessment**

2. List the three Impostor Behaviors that most affect you.

_____

_____

_____

3. For each behavior list examples of when and how they commonly arise and the impact they have on your work and your life.

_____

_____

_____

_____

_____

_____

_____

_____

_____

GUIDED WRITING EXERCISE

Visit composurethebook.com/file to listen to the Brain Hack guided meditation and answer these questions:

1. Imagine a situation in the future that would trigger one of your Impostor Behaviors. Imagine your clone facing that situation. How might your clone handle the situation differently than you would?

_____

_____

_____

_____

_____

_____

_____

_____

_____

_____

_____

_____

_____

_____

2. How would things be different for your clone on the day of the situation, starting in the morning when she or he gets up?

_____

_____

_____

_____

_____

_____

_____

_____

3. Would the fact that the clone did not bring any of the Impostor Behaviors to the situation in any way negatively impact the outcome of the situation? If not, how might that positively impact the outcome?

_____

_____

_____

_____

_____

_____

_____

4. What does the clone know to be true in that situation that you might not usually know to be true (about yourself and your ability to handle the situation)?

_____

_____

_____

_____

_____

_____

5. What does the clone believe to be true that you might not usually believe to be true?

_____

_____

_____

_____

_____

_____

6. If you put the clone in charge three months ago and went on vacation what, if anything, might have gone wrong while your clone was in charge for those months?

_____

_____

_____

_____

_____

_____

_____

7. What advice does your clone have for you?

_____

_____

_____

_____

_____

_____

_____

8. What does your clone grant you permission to do that you might not otherwise do?

_____

_____

_____

_____

_____

_____

_____

_____

9. What one thing does your clone ask that you do differently starting tomorrow?

_____

_____

_____

_____

_____

_____

CHAPTER 3

INTRODUCING EXECUTIVE PRESENCE

———

KEY TAKEAWAYS

Gender Representation

✓ Though women make up more than 50% of college graduates and outperform men, they are remarkably underrepresented in top roles and leadership.

✓ The McKinsey and LeanIn.org Women in the Workplace 2019 report: Female representation falls from around 50% in entry level ranks to about 25% at the executive level and around 7% at the CEO level.

The Confidence Gap

✓ Chamarro-Premuzic's research:

> ▷ Conclusion: "when it comes to leadership, the only advantage that men have over women... is the fact that the manifestations of hubris—often masked as charisma or charm—are commonly mistaken for leadership potential, and that these occur much more frequently in men than in women."

> ▷ The confidence gap between men and women: in just about any industry, men overestimate their own intelligence, while women are generally more humble than men.

> ▷ The best leaders are typically humble, a trait tied to high emotional intelligence, which is more prevalent in women.

✓ A key to being promoted into the executive ranks lies not just in one's abilities, but also in our perception of those abilities.

✓ Self-confidence is extremely important when considering whom to promote for leadership roles, but Executive Presence is essential to gain access to C-level roles.

Executive Presence

✓ Executive Presence is best described as a mature self-confidence that inspires trust in your leadership. It's the ability to take control of difficult situations, make tough decisions, and hold your own with talented and strong-willed colleagues—all while staying calm and composed.

✓ We associate five key abilities with Executive Presence:

▷ **Confidence:** Project a solid sense of self-esteem that ensures your capacity to deal with challenges.

▷ **Composure:** Control your emotions, recognize emotion in others, and effectively manage outcomes.

▷ **Credibility:** Create global trust in your skills and abilities.

▷ **Clarity:** Communicate clearly and concisely.

▷ **Connection:** Interact with others easily to instill faith in your leadership.

✓ Executive Presence is the X factor people need to succeed, not only productively, but also with joy.

✓ When people elevate their confidence and composure, improve clarity and communication, deepen their connections with others, and boost personal credibility, they are more qualified than ever before to become the next generation of leaders the world needs.

Rule of 3

Whenever you're asked a tough question:

1. Take a breath and count backward from three to one.

2. Start your response with, "There are three things to consider..."

3. Give an answer for the first thing, and as you talk come up with the other two.

4. If you can only come up with two, simply say, "In reflection, those two are the most important."

1. Rate your Executive Presence skills on a scale of 1 to 5, 1 = not at all competent, 5 = very competent:

    Confidence: Project a solid sense of self-esteem that ensures your capacity to deal with challenges.

    ⭕——⭕——⭕——⭕——⭕

    NOT AT ALL COMPETENT   VERY COMPETENT

    Composure: Control your emotions, recognize emotion in others, and effectively manage outcomes.

    ⭕——⭕——⭕——⭕——⭕

    NOT AT ALL COMPETENT   VERY COMPETENT

    Credibility: Create global trust in your skills and abilities.

    ⭕——⭕——⭕——⭕——⭕

    NOT AT ALL COMPETENT   VERY COMPETENT

    Clarity: Communicate clearly and concisely.

    ⭕——⭕——⭕——⭕——⭕

    NOT AT ALL COMPETENT   VERY COMPETENT

    Connection: Interact with others easily to instill faith in your leadership.

    ⭕——⭕——⭕——⭕——⭕

    NOT AT ALL COMPETENT   VERY COMPETENT

2. Which three Executive Presence skills do you most want to improve?

_____

_____

_____

3. For each of the three above, give an example of an area of your work in which improving that skill would be beneficial, and what outcomes might be possible when you improve your Executive Presence in that area.

_____

_____

_____

_____

_____

_____

_____

_____

_____

_____

_____

_____

CHAPTER 4

POWERFUL INTENTIONS

KEY TAKEAWAYS

The Journey

✓ The three phases of the journey to break through the Impostor Syndrome are:

▷ *Awareness* - Discover the root causes of Impostor Behaviors and develop self-awareness so that you begin to notice when they appear and how they impact your work and your life.

▷ *Resolution* - Resolve your Impostor Behaviors by developing strong personal boundaries and elevating your Executive Presence.

▷ *Transformation* - Shift your motivation from external to internal to increase congruence with true self and prioritize your own interests, curiosity and passion over those of others.

Powerful Intentions

✓ Powerful intentions serve as a *North Star* to keep you focused and motivated towards your goals. The three characteristics of a powerful intention:

▷ Stated in the positive

▷ Independently achievable and sustainable

▷ Defined by specific, measurable experiences and outcomes

✓ Stated in the Positive: There are two types of intentions:

▷ *Toward* intentions are stated in the positive as something you really desire and can move toward to achieve it.

▷ *Away From* intentions are stated in the negative, something you would like to avoid and move away from.

▷ To transform an *Away From* to a *Toward* intention ask yourself "What would I like instead?" or "If I were not experiencing or feeling that (negative) thing, what would I be experiencing or feeling instead?"

✓ Independently Achievable and Sustainable

▷ An independently achievable intention is solely within your control. It does not require someone else to change or behave in a different way.

▷ To create an independently achievable and sustainable intention ask yourself "Assuming the situation doesn't change, or another person doesn't change or behave differently, what would I like to feel or experience?"

▷ Defined by specific, measurable experiences and outcomes

⊳ The more specific you are about your intention, the more you'll discover what it is you really want, and the greater the likelihood you'll get it. Ask yourself three questions:

1. What would I really like?

2. What will having that do for me?

3. How will I know when I have that?

As-If Frame

✓ The As-If frame helps you further clarify your intention and give your psyche an experience of already having achieved success.

✓ Acting As-If allows you to explore future possibilities internally, without having to first experience the outcome in the physical world.

Visionaries

▷ Visionaries are rare, between 4-8% of the population.

▷ Visionaries are focused on the future, imagining future experience with all five senses to make them feel real.

▷ For visionaries, their future vision pulls them into the future from the present non-linearly rather than linearly.

▷ Once visionaries have experienced the future they are compelled to act because they become impatient with the present.

As-If Frame:

Steps to create the As-If Frame:

1. Imagine you're several months in the future and you've made all the changes you only dreamed about many months ago when you established a new intention.

2. Notice that you have all the solutions, behaviors and responses that you desired.

3. What does a day in the future look like with all this in place?

Awareness of Impostor Behaviors – A One-Week Practice

For the next week, as you go through your days, keep a running list of the things you're starting to notice about your Impostor Behaviors and how they may affect your work and your life. Each time you notice that you're experiencing an Impostor Behavior, pause by silently counting backward from three (3-2-1), and take three calming breaths.

1. During the week, list each instance when you noticed your Impostor Behaviors.

_____

_____

_____

_____

2. What did you notice when you paused and breathed when you experienced an Impostor Behavior?

_____

_____

_____

_____

_____

_____

_____

Create a Powerful Intention

1. State your intention. What would you like?

_____

_____

_____

_____

_____

2. Is your intention stated in the positive? Is it something you would like to move toward rather than move away from or avoid? If not, restate your intention by asking yourself "What would I like instead?" When you're no longer having the experience that you don't want, what will be happening? What's the opposite of what you don't want?

_____

_____

_____

_____

_____

_____

_____

3. Is your intention solely within your control, or does it require someone else to change or behave differently? If it's not solely in your control, ask yourself "What would I like instead if the situation doesn't change or another person doesn't act differently? What would I like then?"

_____

_____

_____

_____

_____

_____

_____

4. How is your intention important to you? What will having your intention do for you?

_____

_____

_____

_____

_____

_____

_____

_____

5. When you have exactly what you would like, how will you know? What will be happening in your life? What positive experiences will you be having that are different from today?

_____

_____

_____

_____

_____

_____

_____

_____

_____

_____

_____

_____

_____

_____

_____

GUIDED WRITING EXERCISE

The guided exercise for the As-If frame takes about 10-15 minutes. Before you begin, make sure you're in a place where you won't be interrupted. As you listen to the guided exercise, don't worry about writing down your thoughts or answering the questions. When the exercise is complete you will have an opportunity to answer the questions in order to capture your experience.

Visit composurethebook.com/file to listen to the guided meditation

Imagine you're several months out. You have made all the changes in your life that you only dreamed about back when you were setting your intention. But now you have the solutions, behaviors, and responses that you desired, even though originally you weren't exactly sure about what you wanted. Imagine a day in your future life and take yourself for a test drive, from the moment you wake up to the moment you go to bed.

1. From this place in the future, what might a typical day look like now?

_____

_____

_____

_____

_____

_____

_____

_____

_____

_____

2. How do you feel about yourself?

_____

_____

_____

_____

_____

_____

_____

_____

3. If you could see yourself walking down the street, what would you look like?

_____

_____

_____

_____

_____

_____

_____

_____

_____

4. What might you be wearing?

_____

_____

_____

_____

5. What kinds of people might you be meeting and having lunch or dinners with?

_____

_____

_____

_____

6. From this place in the future, what might you believe to be true about yourself that you didn't believe before?

_____

_____

_____

_____

_____

_____

_____

7. From this place in the future, what might you believe to be true about the world that you didn't believe before?

_____

_____

_____

_____

_____

_____

8. Does this future experience lead to anything unexpected?

_____

_____

_____

_____

_____

_____

POWERFUL INTENTIONS

BodyFlow Series

Visit composurethebook.com/file to experience the Powerful Intentions BodyFlow video

It takes about 15 minutes. This BodyFlow video is a powerful tool designed to strengthen and integrate your powerful intention in your system so that you increase the likelihood of success.

CHAPTER 5

THE ROOT CAUSE

KEY TAKEAWAYS

External Validation

✓ Impostor Behaviors arise from an over reliance on external validation, resulting in a weak and under-developed sense of self.

✓ This behavior is common among perfectionists who worry unnecessarily about the quality of their work.

✓ An over reliance on external validation often emerges from childhood and can be the result of several things, including family dynamics and childhood experiences, trauma, limiting societal norms, and even from being a gifted child.

Limiting Behavior Patterns

✓ You have to develop an awareness of a deeply entrenched behavioral pattern and eliminate the resistance to it before you can do anything about it. The key is to step back and observe it with curiosity and compassion.

✓ These behavioral patterns are designed to protect you and keep you safe. When you observe it objectively and compassionately, then you can ask yourself whether it's really needed, or if it's just an old response that's running on autopilot.

Root Causes

✓ Difficult Childhood Experiences

  ▷ Difficult childhood experiences often result in an acute awareness of external authority. And when that happens, children such as this grow into adults who ignore their own personal instincts and instead seek approval outside of themselves.

  ▷ This is especially true for children who felt they had something to prove while growing up, or those who overcame challenges in school, family dynamics, or both.

  ▷ Childhood experiences that often lead to an over reliance on external validation:

    ▸ Children who struggle with learning difficulties

- ⯈ Families in which children were caretakers for their parents or siblings

- ⯈ Families that don't allow children to embrace their intelligence and shine

✓ Giftedness

- ▷ We see a high correlation between high performers who are gifted at something and the Impostor Syndrome.

- ▷ Gifted children have the capability to perform at higher levels in one or more domains compared to others of the same age, experience level, and environment.

- ▷ Giftedness is found within all racial, ethnic and cultural populations, as well as economic strata.

- ▷ Gifted children are, by definition, kids who perform exceptionally well intellectually, academically, creatively, and artistically.

- ▷ Gifted children have greater intellectual processing capacity than their peers. The neurons in the brain of the gifted child seem to be bio-chemically more abundant and thus are able to process more complex thoughts.

- ▷ They also demonstrate greater prefrontal cortex activity in the brain, which indicates a capacity for more insightful and intuitive thinking and curiosity.

- ▷ They also demonstrate more alpha wave activity, which allows for more relaxed and focused learning. This leads to greater memory retention and integration.

- ▷ There can be a downside to being gifted. Research also indicates that gifted individuals tend to be emotionally sensitive and empathic, making normal environments more stressful.

- ▷ They often feel as if they're held to higher standards than their peers, and can be anxious and find it difficult to accept criticism and experience rejection as emotionally painful.

- ▷ Gifted children may find it harder to develop a sense of belonging and may often feel as if they simply don't fit in, leading them to often feel isolated and misunderstood as children and as adults.

✓ Trauma

- ▷ Almost all of our unwanted behaviors and experiences can be traced back to family dynamics or trauma we endured at the hands of loving, but often flawed, parents or primary caregivers.

▷ Exploring how your early childhood impacts your adult life is not an indictment of you or your parents, or how you were raised. It is instead a way to forge a deeper understanding about yourself.

▷ Unconscious patterns that arise as a result of childhood experiences underpin much of your behavior and belief system today.

▷ This awareness gives you the freedom to make better choices, especially in response to challenging situations and environments where you don't feel psychologically safe. In our early years, our very survival depends on the physical and emotional care we receive from our parents (or adults in a parental position). Consistently feeling loved, valued, supported, and accepted for who we are through unconditional love by our parents and caregivers leads to strong emotional health and well-being in adulthood.

▷ Young children who experience a parents' anger, depression, abandonment, or even death feel that love has been withheld and that the parental bond has been broken, leading to feeling of shame, of being unlovable and unsafe.

▷ Children are egocentric; when a parent is not present, physically or mentally, they feel as though they are worth less than their parents' time, attention, or direction causing shame and decisions about themselves being "bad" or "not good enough."

▷ Factors that produce parental insecurity include: a lack of emotional warmth and safe touch, inconsistent and erratic behavior, punitive and punishing caregiving, broken promises, over-nurturing and over-protective caregiving, a lack of patience, a lack of tolerance and respect for the child's needs, a lack of encouragement to try new things, too much admiration for achievements and not enough acknowledgement of effort, having to take sides in parental disagreements, too much or too little responsibility, shame and isolation, and racial, gender or cultural injustice, and discrimination.

▷ Parentification is the process of role reversal between parent and child in which the child is required to act as a parent to their parent or siblings. In some cases, the child fills the void of an absent, incapacitated or estranged spouse to support the other parent's emotional life.

✓ Limiting Societal Norms

▷ Limiting societal norms fuel much of the inequity that "out groups" experience.

▷ A 2001 research study on entitlement showed that both men and women performed roughly the same, and both believed they performed worse than their peers on a task, but the women paid themselves just *half* of what the men did.

▷ Women's self-pay was based on how they perceived their own performance.

▷ Men's feelings of self-esteem had the biggest impact on self-pay.

The Entitlement Gap

✓ In the 1960s the word "entitlement" became associated with government benefits such as Medicaid and food stamps, which effectively shifted our society's sentiments, associations, and definitions of the concept, relating entitlement to a *handout*.

✓ In our work, we support the notion of "healthy" entitlement.

✓ According to an oft-cited Hewlett Packard internal report, men apply for a job when they meet sixty percent of the qualifications, but women apply only if they meet one hundred percent.

✓ Women's depressed sense of entitlement is rooted in the idea that they must base their entitlement to advance on past performance, whereas men tend not to believe this.

✓ To achieve gender equality in promotion and advancement, we need to find ways to elevate women to healthy levels of entitlement, similar to those of their male peers.

✓ A recent study conducted by PayScale found that (in most industries) when people agree or strongly agree that their organization is transparent in how pay is determined, then the gender pay gap closes at all levels.

✓ The same concept of transparency used to close the gender pay gap could also be applied to closing the advancement gap.

✓ Possible solutions to the gender pay and advancement gaps:

▷ Transparency in pay equity and advancement practices.

▷ Opening a dialogue between men and women to help women understand how men assess their readiness for promotion and advancement.

▷ Call upon men to advocate for high-performing female colleagues when they're ready to step up in their careers.

✓ When we elevate women to a healthy sense of entitlement, we level the playing field.

✓ One's sense of entitlement can also be rooted in trauma and childhood experience.

TOOLS

Find Your Butt

Whenever your body kicks into high gear panic, drop your awareness into your body and breathe. We call this *finding your butt*.

1. When anxiety and panic take over, we stop breathing and our bodies tense up so much that if you sit, for example, your full weight isn't in the chair. It's actually you physically supporting yourself, not the chair. When you stop, take deep breaths, and become aware of feeling the weight of your butt in the chair, you can consciously release your weight, so that you relax and start to calm your breath.

2. Once that happens, observe the changes in your body with curiosity and compassion.

3. Take a moment to consider, "Is what I'm feeling right now helpful? Is it needed? Or is it just an overreaction?"

4. Don't forget to BREATHE.

Butterfly Tapping

To calm and soothe yourself:

1. Stop and breathe, in through your nose and out through your mouth.

2. Feel the weight of your body in your chair and notice your breath going in and out.

3. Cross your arms and lightly tap your hands on each opposite arm while you breathe.

4. You can also rest your hands on your thighs and slowly and gently alternate tapping each thigh.

5. You can also slowly and gently alternate tapping each foot on the ground.

WRITING EXERCISE

1. List any situations or dynamics in your life where you often experience an over reliance on external validation.

_____

_____

_____

_____

_____

_____

_____

2. Looking at those situations or dynamics, is there a connection between those and experiences from your childhood?

_____

_____

_____

_____

_____

_____

_____

3. Which, if any, of their common causes of an over reliance on external validation do you most relate to (difficult childhood experiences, giftedness, trauma, limiting social norms)?

_____

_____

_____

_____

_____

4. Imagine a situation in which Impostor Behavior(s) is/are triggered because of hyper vigilance or an over reliance on external validation.

_____

_____

_____

_____

5. What might be the positive intention of that behavior?

_____

_____

_____

_____

_____

6. When you imagine that situation, what are the emotions associated with it?

_____

_____

_____

_____

7. Where do you feel it in your body? Describe the feeling (sharp/dull, pulsing/solid, heavy/
   light, ...).

_____

_____

_____

_____

8. As you feel the feeling, scan back in your childhood and take notice of times in your past
   when you've experienced a similar feeling. List a few of these times.

_____

_____

_____

_____

_____

9. How do you feel about the word "entitlement"?

_____

_____

_____

10. What might a sense of "healthy entitlement" mean for you? In what areas of your life would you like to feel greater entitlement (deservingness)?

_____

_____

_____

_____

_____

11. Imagine what a day in your life might be like if you felt a healthy sense of entitlement in all of the areas where you would benefit.

_____

_____

_____

_____

_____

CHAPTER 6

BADASS BOUNDARIES

_____

KEY TAKEAWAYS

Time Management

✓ How you use your time is a reflection of your priorities, and you are in control of your priorities more than you think! We can make choices to determine what we *will* do given our finite amount of time and energy. These choices are our priorities.

✓ Imagine if every time you told yourself '*I don't have time to do that thing,*' you instead rephrased it to '*That thing is not a priority.*'

✓ Our priorities become more manageable when we establish personal boundaries.

Personal Boundaries

✓ Personal boundaries are the limits that we establish in our relationships; they reflect what we feel we're entitled to. Our boundaries determine what we're willing to give (or tolerate) without compromising our physical, emotional, and spiritual well-being.

✓ Our boundaries are somatic, meaning they live in our bodies. They are a *felt sense* of where we end and others begin.

✓ Your personal boundary creates a protected, sacred space around you, in which *you and only you* get to decide what gets in and what stays out.

✓ Boundaries are badass when they allow us to say 'No' or 'Back off' to things we don't want and when they encourage us to say 'Yes' or '*I can*' to what we really, really want!

✓ Your ability to know and assert your boundaries reflects a healthy sense of self-worth, ensuring that you're not subject to other people's judgement, expectations, and needs.

✓ If you're curious where you may lack robust personal boundaries, simply consider areas of your life where you wish others would treat you differently.

Triggers

✓ Triggers are emotional reactions that are out of proportion to the situation.

✓ We are triggered when our mental and emotional boundaries are not sufficiently strong and we instantly (and unconsciously) internalize things such as unwelcome requests, judgement, criticism, problems, unexpected feelings, or the emotions of others.

✓ We are triggered by things we experience as a threat, which in turn trigger a fight-flight-freeze response.

✓ Even though you've evolved, there is still a reptilian part of your brain that spontaneously responds to triggers as if your life were threatened by a predator.

✓ Triggers are reactions to boundary violations.

✓ It's incredibly common for our clients to struggle with saying "no" to what they don't want.

✓ Saying "no" sets limits for what you take on, including when and how you work. People often take on more than they're actually comfortable doing when they find it difficult to say "no" because they overemphasize external feedback and seek approval and to avoid criticism. This creates anxiety and leads to burnout.

Fight, Flight, Freeze

✓ Fight or flight is a primitive survival instinct that results in instant hormonal and physiological changes designed to get you to act quickly to protect yourself.

✓ In fight or flight, your heart rate goes up, which increases the oxygen flow to your major muscles so you can take quick action. Your pain perception drops, and your hearing sharpens due to the adrenaline that courses through your veins.

✓ Freeze occurs when your body releases the stress hormones adrenaline and cortisol to get you away from a perceived threat and into safety. This reaction lasts around 30 seconds, yet the fear doesn't go away. As a result, the parasympathetic nervous system counterbalances the physical effects of stress by slowing down your heart rate and your breathing, often to the point of holding your breath, as if your body freezes in a motionless state of protection against a future threat.

✓ When people are triggered we teach them to BREATHE so they can reset their nervous systems away from fear and freeze and into feeling safe again.

✓ Strengthening your personal boundaries can greatly reduce your tendency to be triggered into fight-flight-freeze mode.

Bi-Lateral Brain Stimulation – Butterfly Tapping

✓ Alternating butterfly tapping stimulates both sides of the brain. It's used in Eye Movement Desensitization and Reprocessing (EMDR) therapy to help clients find a resourceful place in their bodies so they can safely process fears or worries of future problems, as well as traumatic memories.

✓ Butterfly Tapping can also be used in day-to-day situations to calm and ground yourself.

✓ Bilateral stimulation opens the lines of communication between the brain hemispheres to engage the whole brain.

✓ When we experience emotionally charged memories and thoughts, we do so with just one brain hemisphere activated. The other hemisphere shuts down so the mind can focus on acting quickly in a fight-flight situation. When we butterfly tap, we activate both sides of the brain while relaxing the body.

✓ By reducing the emotional charge on the thoughts and recollections held in working memory, we actually alter older memories with a newly updated experience through bilateral stimulation.

Boundary Violations

✓ We first learn about our boundaries as the result of how our parents or caregivers relate to us as infants and children.

✓ All infants have natural rhythms for desired connection and disconnection. It gives an infant or child a sense of safety and well-being when a parent or caregiver is responsive and honors their cues for connection and disconnection.

✓ No parent is perfect. When parents misunderstand a child's cues it can rupture a child's sense of personal boundary.

✓ Ruptures are a normal part of parenting and can strengthen a child's resilience and stress tolerance so long as the caregiver successfully repairs the injury to re-establish safety and reconnection.

✓ Infants coo or smile to express a desire for connection. On the other hand, they avert their gaze or turn their head to the side when they need to disconnect.

✓ Research shows that depressed mothers are less likely to be attuned to a child's cues for connection or disconnection, and therefore more likely to violate boundaries.

✓ Having poor boundaries, and the resulting propensity to be easily triggered, can emerge as a result of the boundary violations we experienced as children.

✓ Three common patterns of boundary violations:

    ▷ Invasion – when a caregiver misreads signals for disconnection and does not recognize the children's need for space.

- In some, invasion can be fueled by a caregiver's own need to feel loved, or as the result of abuse.

- Those who felt invaded as children develop a rigid boundary style to protect their most vulnerable feelings.

- As adults these individuals can become isolated and develop extreme independence.

▷ Abandonment – results when a caregiver is not responsive to signals for connection.

- With abandonment children learn to override their natural need for connection and instead develop an instinct to seek connection at any cost.

- These individuals tend to overly adapt to the needs of others and feel hesitant to set limits with others for fear of rejection.

- They tend to lose their sense of self or take care of others at expense of their own needs in relationships.

▷ Combined Invasion and Abandonment – when a caregiver alternates erratically between being invasive and unresponsive.

- These children cannot develop a reliable strategy to meet their needs.

- They alternate between longing for connection and a desire for disconnection.

Boundary Setting

✓ Boundary setting is critical to manage competing priorities in your life so that you can effectively manage your time.

✓ When you keep a request outside of your boundary and identify the conflict, then sit in silence, you invite the other party to join with you to come up with solutions.

✓ In addition to external feedback and request, you can also put your own unwanted internal feelings and voices outside of your boundaries.

✓ When you resolve unwanted internal feelings and voices it is important to acknowledge their intended positive outcome, and the importance those voices and feelings have had throughout your life.

✓ When we struggle with perfectionism, the internal voice is often asking "have I done enough?" And with our perfectionism in charge the answer is almost always no.

TOOLS

Balancing Breath

To calm and soothe yourself:

1. Breathe in through your nose as you raise your outstretched arms toward the ceiling with palms facing up.

2. Exhale through your mouth as you lower your arms with palms down, like leaves falling off of trees in autumn.

3. Repeat three times.

Establishing a Strong Personal Boundary

Your somatic perception of where you end and where others begin forms your personal boundaries. Your *felt sense* is a key tool to becoming aware of what feels right to you and what feels off.

1. Take three balancing breaths.

2. Put both arms out in front of you with palms facing forward and fingers pointing up, as if you're pushing something away.

3. Look at the back of your hands and imagine that the space between you and the back of your hands is your own sacred, safe space. Nothing gets in that space unless you allow it in. You, and only you, decide what you bring in and what stays outside.

4. Take a deep breath and really feel into that space. Notice how it feels.

5. Slowly move the backs of your hands closer to your body, coming near your chest and shoulders. Look at the back of your hands now that they're closer to you and notice how that feels.

6. Slowly move your hands away from your body again, all the way, and notice how that feels.

7. Think of a situation where you would like to establish a strong personal boundary. Move your hands to find a comfortable place for the space you would like in that situation.

8. Focus on the back of your hands and imagine that situation with this amount of sacred, safe, personal space around you. You only let in what you decide to allow in. Settle into that space and breathe. Notice how that feels.

9. Breathe and integrate that feeling into your system, so that your system will remember *how this feels* the next time you are in that situation.

10. Seal in this feeling by doing Butterfly Tapping for a minute or more.

1. List common situations where you wish someone would treat you differently, especially situations that trigger you.

_____

_____

_____

_____

_____

_____

_____

2. List situations where you have trouble saying "no".

_____

_____

_____

_____

_____

_____

_____

3. For each of the situations above, identify the feeling you have when you experience these situations. You might want to visit this website to refer to the list of emotions: **https://tomdrummond.com/leading-and-caring-for-children/emotion-vocabulary/ emotionvocab/**

_____

_____

_____

_____

_____

_____

_____

_____

_____

_____

_____

_____

_____

_____

_____

4. Do you recall experiencing boundary violations (invasion, abandonment, or both) as a child? If so, how do you think those experiences may impact your adult relationships and behavior?

_____

_____

_____

_____

_____

_____

_____

5. Recall a few times in your past that you felt triggered. For each of these, notice whether you experienced fight, flight, freeze, or some combination of those.

_____

_____

_____

_____

_____

_____

_____

GUIDED WRITING EXERCISE

1. Think of something that has triggered you in the past, especially a common, recurring trigger. (*Example: being asked a question for which you don't know the answer when giving a presentation.*)

2. Imagine that triggering situation. Notice what emotions and feelings you experience, and what bodily sensations go along with those feelings. (*Example: I felt panicked and fearful that I might not have the right answer. I notice my face flushing and my pulse racing.*)

3. Now put both arms out in front of you with palms facing forward and fingers pointing up, as if you're pushing something away. Look at the back of your hands and imagine that the space between you and the back of your hands is your own sacred, safe space. Nothing gets in that space unless you allow it in. You, and only you, decide what you bring in and what stays outside.

4. Imagine moving your trigger, the feelings associated with that trigger, and the bodily sensations associated with that trigger outside your sacred, safe place, on the other side of your upturned palms. You might use your hands to "scoop out" the feelings and sensations from your chest and "push" them outward, breathing out through your mouth as you push them out, saying "back off". Do this several times, breathe and butterfly tap.

5. With the trigger, your feelings and the related bodily sensations outside of your sacred, safe felt space, answer the following questions:

   a. What do you know to be true about the situation? (*Example: I know that I have prepared well for the presentation, and that I have expertise in this area, and when I have answers I will give them, and when I don't it's OK to say "Good question! I don't have that answer at this moment, but I'll get the answer and get back to you by 5pm today."*)

   _____

   _____

   _____

   _____

b. What do you deserve in this situation? What are you entitled to?
(Example: I deserve to be heard and to have people be thoughtful and respectful about what I present. It's OK for me to answer questions for which I know the answer, and if I don't know the answer say I'll get back with an answer at a future date and time.)

_____

_____

_____

_____

c. What is in the highest and best good of all in the situation? In the highest good of you? Of those around you? Of the company or business or situation? (Example: It's in the highest and best good that I do a good job with the presentation. My audience wants me to be effective and to hear what I have to say. It's in the highest and best good for my audience to have an opportunity to ask questions and ask for clarification. It's in the highest and best good that I remain calm and open and curious about their questions, and not get triggered or shut down. It's in the highest and best good for my audience to want me to be effective and clear.)

_____

_____

_____

_____

_____

_____

_____

6. With all of that in mind, imagine that situation with your strong boundaries in place, knowing what you are deserving of and entitled to, and what is in the highest and best good. In what ways might this feel different than what you felt previously, without a strong boundary, sacred and safe space, and all that you know to be true in place? (Example: I feel much more calm and grounded. I am composed even when I imagine being asked difficult questions. I know that most of my colleagues in the audience are supportive and want me to do well. I deserve to not have all the answers, and in those instances I'm responsible for getting back to them promptly.)

_____

_____

_____

_____

_____

_____

_____

_____

7. Breathe and Butterfly Tap.

BodyFlow Series

Visit composurethebook.com/file to experience the Developing Personal Boundaries BodyFlow video

It takes about 15 minutes. This BodyFlow video is a powerful tool designed to strengthen and integrate your powerful intention in your system so that you increase the likelihood of success.

CHAPTER 7

DEALING WITH CONFLICT

KEY TAKEAWAYS

✓ External conflict involves an uncomfortable or difficult situation with another person or group of people.

✓ Dealing effectively with external conflict is critical to Executive Presence.

✓ Internal conflict comes from within when we have conflicting beliefs or needs and keeps us stuck and prevents us from having the outcomes we desire.

✓ Internal Conflict

▷ Conflicting beliefs and needs are different aspects of one's personality, their subpersonalities.

▷ Subpersonalities influence how we feel, perceive, and behave, and they shape our core beliefs and identity.

▷ The inner critic is one common subpersonality that loves to point out all your flaws and mistakes and is a master at undermining your accomplishments.

▷ The inner critic can conflict with your curiosity and willingness to take risks, preventing you from trying new things.

✓ Feeling Stuck

▷ One common internal conflict is feeling stuck, as in situations we know what we would like to do (or even what we should do), but we can't seem to make ourselves do it.

▷ To work through the conflict, we need to explore the unconscious half of the conflict that keeps us stuck.

▷ To do this we curiously explore the intentions of each side of the conflict, and, importantly, appreciate the powerful good of both.

✓ On the One Hand, On the Other Hand is a technique designed to resolve inner conflict.

▷ We often use disassociation to work with challenging or emotionally difficult topics to see the situation from afar, which allows us to be less triggered and more curious and resourceful.

▷ Metaphors are tools to shift our perspective from associated to disassociated.

▷ The *"on the one hand, on the other hand"* exercise works because it provides three steps as important tools that can help you overcome internal conflict. These steps are:

  ▹ Identify and name both sides of the conflict.

  ▹ Appreciate the positive intentions of both sides of the conflict (often they are two different approaches to the same or similar outcomes).

  ▹ Determine a solution that satisfies the needs of both sides of the conflict.

✓ Work-Life Balance

▷ Trying to accommodate the conflicting desires of investing time and energy in work, but still somehow carve out enough time and energy for a personal and family life can seem nearly impossible.

▷ Perfectionism can make this conflict worse, as the desire for perfectionism leads to overwork and overpreparation, which consumes time that could otherwise be spent for self and family.

✓ Resistance

▷ There are times when internal resistance is so great that it prevents the objects in each hand from coming together.

▷ This alternative outcome is completely fine and can actually provide its own insights and discernments.

▷ Resistance can result when the desired resolution to the conflict threatens safety and well-being, whether it's perceived or real.

✓ External Conflict

▷ If you get ahead of external conflict, sometimes you can minimize or even prevent it.

▷ You can use the *"on the one hand, on the other hand"* technique for external conflict to clearly articulate the positive and negative aspects of the conflict.

▷ The three-chair exercise can be effective to provide insights and perspective that will be helpful to resolve an external conflict. It looks at a conflict situation from three different angles

  ▷ From your own self-interest (associate into yourself)

  ▷ From the other person's interest (dissociate from yourself and associate into the another person)

  ▷ From a *higher authority* (dissociate from yourself and associate into a neutral third party)

TOOLS

Giving Critical Feedback

When giving critical feedback it's best to start with positive acknowledgement, and then highlight the negative or constructive feedback.

State the feedback in the form of: On the One Hand (positive, acknowledgement) ...On the Other Hand (negative, criticism or feedback).

For example, *"Bill, on the one hand I really like your dedication to the business and your efforts to get things done fast. On the other hand, it is important that we do the full due diligence on this acquisition to ensure that we do not expose the business to too much risk, therefore I am proposing that we delay the next meeting by one week."*

WRITING EXERCISE

GUIDED WRITING EXERCISE

On the One Hand, On the Other Hand is a technique to resolve conflict using metaphorical symbols and somatic movement. **Visit composurethebook.com/file to access the guided audio version of this exercise.**

1. Define the inner conflict in a single sentence using the phrase "on the one hand ... on the other hand..." *(Example: On the one hand I want to push for a promotion, and on the other hand I want to avoid potential rejection and failure and disappointment.)*

_____

_____

_____

_____

2. What two words represent the conflicting desires? *(Example: "ambitious" and "safe.")*

_____

_____

_____

_____

3. Turn your palms upward and hold them in front of you, cupping your hands. Imagine that you put each word into each one of your hands.

4. Imagine an object that best represents the concept behind each word. It's usually best to choose the first thing that comes to mind.

_____

_____

_____

_____

_____

5. Appreciate the positive intention of each object. For each object, what is the good it wishes to bring to you? Even if it is creating something you don't like, look for the positive intention behind what it's creating.

_____

_____

_____

_____

_____

6. What has the intention of each object meant for you throughout your life? How have they shaped the person you are today?

_____

_____

_____

_____

_____

7. Think of a character name for each object.

_____

_____

_____

_____

8. Ask each object if they are willing to work together to help you resolve your inner conflict. Remind them how much you appreciate the good they are trying to bring to you, and promise them that you won't demote either one, instead you will look for ways to make them even more effective.

   Ask them if they're willing to do that. If either is unwilling to work together, go back to step 5 and further explore and acknowledge the positive intention of the resistant object. Reassure the resistant object that it gets veto power on any solutions, and that you can always keep things the way they are if the resistant object is not in support of the proposed solution.

9. For each object, what is the good that object wants for you? And what will having that good do for you? And what will having that do for you? Ask the last question and write down the answers three times. (Example: Hannah (the warm blanket) wants three things: to keep me safe, protect me from rejection, and protect me from failure. Having that will make me feel calm and happy, and that brings me happiness and peace.)

_____

_____

_____

_____

_____

10. Do the two objects desire similar things for you, but are using different strategies to get those outcomes? How so?

_____

_____

_____

_____

11. Ask the objects again whether they are willing to work together to come to a common positive outcome. If not, ask the resisting object(s) what are their concerns.

12. Once you have agreement to work together, turn your palms to face each other, and slowly bring them together until you enclose the two objects in your palms with both hands. You will notice that sometimes you will actually feel resistance, like two repelling magnets. That's normal. When that happens don't force it. Just stop and breathe, and when the resistance fades continue to move your palms closer together.

13. Once your hands come together, with your palms together just breathe for a minute.

14. When your hands bring the objects together, how does it feel? (*Example: Super calm and much less heavy.*)

_____

_____

_____

_____

15. Did the objects change in any way when they came together in your palms? If so, how?

_____

_____

_____

_____

_____

_____

16. Now imagine a situation where the inner conflict would normally arise. With these two objects together how might that situation feel or be different now that the objects have become aligned and opened space for a new approach? (Example: I'll start to research how I could approach getting a promotion and when needed, I can always retreat to my warm blanket to recharge and weather the fear and uncertainty.)

_____

_____

_____

_____

_____

_____

Perceptual Positions

An exercise with three chairs to look at a conflict situation from three different angles. **Visit composurethebook.com/file to access a guided audio of this exercise.**

1. Set up two chairs facing each other and a third off to the side.

2. Sit in one of the facing chairs, close your eyes and drop into the moment when you'll deal with the conflict, fully embodied in yourself. Imagine giving the opening statement you'd make to start the discussion. What do you notice in yourself as you sit in that chair and start the discussion? (*Example: I'm really nervous.*)

_____

_____

_____

_____

3. Shake out your arms and hands, and recite your phone number backward to clear your mind.

4. Now stand up and go sit down in the chair facing you where the other person would sit. Picture yourself breathing through their lungs, and looking out through their eyes. When you're ready, give your opening, but react to it as if you're the one hearing it across from your chair. What do you notice as you sit in the chair of the other person and hear your opening? (*Example: I feel tense, almost panicked. I'm nervous about the situation. I don't know if there is a good way to resolve this situation, so I'm worried about our relationship and that you'll be angry with me.*)

_____

_____

_____

_____

5. Now shake that off, and sit in the third chair as a neutral third party that has in mind the best interests of you both. Let's see what that neutral third person has to say about the situation. What advice might this person give you about how to approach the conversation? From this situation what is in the highest and best good? (Example: *I could start by acknowledging that the person I'm dealing with is in a difficult spot, and that this is a challenging dynamic, but that I believe we can work through this and get to a good outcome together. What's in the highest and best good is that we deal respectfully and truthfully with one another, and that we set our differences aside to try to understand where the other is coming from so we can find a solution that works for both of us.*)

_____

_____

_____

_____

_____

_____

6. Now shake that off and go back to the first chair. This time modify the opening to integrate what you've learned. How does it feel this time from the first chair, as yourself?

_____

_____

_____

_____

_____

7. Now shake that off and go to the second chair, and imagine you're listening to the modified opening. How does it feel this time from the second chair, hearing it from the perspective of the other party?

_____

_____

_____

_____

_____

_____

_____

BodyFlow Series

<u>Visit composurethebook.com/file to experience the Resolving Conflict BodyFlow video</u>

It takes about 15 minutes. This BodyFlow video is a powerful tool designed to strengthen and integrate your powerful intention in your system so that you increase the likelihood of success.

CHAPTER 8

REVISE
LIMITING
BELIEFS

———

KEY TAKEAWAYS

Beliefs

✓ Beliefs are energy-saving shortcuts we use to predict our environment.

✓ Beliefs are mental representations of the patterns our brain expects, which let us know what we can expect in our environment, and how things should relate to each other.

✓ Our system of beliefs and convictions motivate our performance, decision making and sense of self. Combined they determine what we feel we deserve and are entitled to.

✓ Beliefs shape our ability to deal with stress, as well as the development and design of our plans, goals, and needs. They shape the perceptions of who we are and what we deserve and can positively or negatively shape the reality we create for ourselves.

Confirmation Bias

✓ When we harbor a firm belief, even massive information to the contrary will not sway us. We ignore and filter it out in favor of the more belief-affirming information.

✓ Our brain's preference for familiarity and eagerness for efficiency makes it prone to error, preferring to fit new information into existing frameworks rather than reconstruct new ones from scratch.

✓ Confirmation bias is the process by which we favor information or experiences that confirm our beliefs.

Safety Patterning

✓ Safety Patterning is the set of beliefs we develop in childhood as a means of keeping us safe, typically imprinted when we experience fear, trauma or shame.

✓ Safety Patterns often operate unconsciously and can go largely unexamined even over a lifetime.

Changing Beliefs

✓ While people perceive the process of changing beliefs to be difficult and taxing, we naturally change dozens if not hundreds of beliefs throughout our lifetime.

✓ Beliefs change when a new experience emerges to destabilize an existing belief.

✓ Beliefs cycle through in three phases that are like the changing of seasons:

  ▷ What we want to believe.

  ▷ What we actually believe.

  ▷ What we used to believe.

✓ To shift beliefs, a first important step is to create awareness to bring them out from the unconscious to the conscious.

Limiting Beliefs

✓ Limiting beliefs are unconscious patterns that hold us back and get in the way of what we'd like to accomplish.

✓ It rarely works to attempt to change a limiting belief by repressing them or trying to convince yourself they're not true. The only way to change a belief is to destabilize the belief using the part(s) of your system that hold(s) the belief(s) in place.

Core Beliefs

✓ Core beliefs are a person's unique central ideas about themselves, others and the world. Core beliefs can cause different people to experience and react to situations very differently.

✓ Core beliefs are typically formed in childhood, usually brought on by an extreme emotional response to an experience, or a trauma, such as the unexpected death of a loved one, an illness, or a near-death experience.

✓ Our reactions to core beliefs are deeply entrenched responses designed to keep us safe by changing our behavior to avoid potential harm—such as a fight or flight response.

✓ The core beliefs that are most deeply held and difficult to change are often imprinted with the emotions of shame and guilt.

✓ Shame and guilt are so powerful because they have the potential to threaten two of our most core needs—the need to belong, and the need to be loved.

✓ Perfectionism is a core belief rooted in self-worth—in other words to be worthy I must be perfect.

TOOLS

Freewriting

Freewriting is similar to brainstorming but is written in sentence and paragraph form *without stopping*. It is an effective technique to shut down your "inner censor" and experience writing in the state of flow. Freewriting is a fast way of thinking on paper. It enables you to reach a level of thinking that's often difficult to attain during the course of a normal business day. This technique helps you understand the world, spot opportunities and options, solve problems, create ideas, and make decisions. Freewriting can also be used to release pent-up thoughts, worries and concerns.

1. Choose a writing prompt or topic.

2. Choose the amount of time you'd like to freewrite and set a timer.

3. Start writing (we recommend pen and paper vs. on a computer) and write continuously without stopping or lifting the pen from paper. Even if you don't know what to write, keep going. For example, if your mind goes blank, you can write 'thinking... don't know what to write... still thinking.'

4. Write as fast as your hand moves when you scribble a note to someone.

1. What childhood or earlier life experiences contribute to your negative or limiting beliefs? Which of these experiences are still likely to occur or are relevant today?

_____

_____

_____

_____

_____

2. Think of two or three old beliefs you no longer have. For each, think about how the belief changed. Were there new experiences you began to have or was there new information you began to notice when your belief changed? Is it possible that those experiences or the information were there but went unnoticed prior to the belief changing?

_____

_____

_____

_____

_____

_____

_____

3. Think of something that you would like to do, but is challenging for you, or that you resist doing. Make a list of the beliefs that you believe to be true about the situation you'd like to do, both good and bad. (Example: I'd like to develop a regular morning routine of doing a short set of yoga stretches and meditating for 10 minutes. What the beliefs I have about this are: that yoga and meditation are good for me and will make me more grounded and happier; that I need to wake up earlier to do this and I'm struggling to get enough sleep; that I won't have time to answer emails if I leave them for my workday so I'll be stressed; that I struggle every time I try to make a new, healthy routine.)

_____

_____

_____

_____

_____

_____

4. When you think about your struggle with this thing you'd like to do but is challenging for you, what feelings does it evoke? Where do you feel it in your body?

_____

_____

_____

_____

_____

_____

5. When you are able to consistently do the thing that you'd like to do, what new beliefs might you have? What experiences would go with those beliefs? (Example: I will believe that I have a successful regular morning practice that I love. I will believe that when I'm tired or stressed that my morning practice will actually bring energy and positive feelings and make that better and give me a better start to the day. I will be more energetic, grounded and calm. Little things that used to set me off won't bother me.)

_____

_____

_____

_____

_____

_____

_____

_____

_____

REVISE LIMITING BELIEFS

BodyFlow Series

Visit composurethebook.com/file to experience the Revise Limiting Beliefs BodyFlow videos

It takes about 15 minutes. This BodyFlow video is a powerful tool designed to strengthen and integrate your powerful intention in your system so that you increase the likelihood of success.

CHAPTER 9

RESOLVING TRAUMA

—

KEY TAKEAWAYS

Trauma

- ✓ We think of trauma as a word that starts with a capital "T" like the death of a parent, or a devastating accident, or your family home burning down.

- ✓ Trauma can also start with a little "t" like being bullied at school, enduring shame, or even breaking your arm.

- ✓ The impact of the trauma all depends on the emotional context in which your system processes the event. But even small events that cause extreme emotional reactions—particularly shame—can trigger trauma.

- ✓ It's a safety mechanism to ensure survival. Our bodies hold onto traumatic memories to protect us from future harm and damage. And yet, our bodies activate our trauma response whether or not our perception of danger is accurate or inaccurate, real or imagined.

- ✓ *"Traumatic events overwhelm the ordinary systems of care that give people a sense of control, connection and meaning."* – Dr. Judith Herman, author of *Trauma and Recovery*

- ✓ *"Remember that dangerous can mean more than just a threat to the well-being of the body. It can also mean a threat to what we do, say, think, care about, believe in, or yearn for."* – Resmaa Menakem, author of *My Grandmother's Hands*

Symptoms of Trauma

- ✓ Trauma can stem from a one-time event or be the result of an ongoing experience, anything from abuse or serious injury, to violence or war.

- ✓ Trauma can cause a lifetime of hypervigilance and flashbacks, resulting depression, mood disorders, psychosomatic issues, and substance abuse.

- ✓ Trauma can be defined as an overwhelming experience in which we lose our connection with what is safe. As a result, traumatized people are often unable to take action to heal. They feel helpless, broken, unwanted, and inadequate.

✓ Reactions to trauma vary. One person's response to trauma might be anxiety, insomnia, or feeling disconnected, while someone else might feel confused, withdrawn, or have intrusive thoughts.

✓ A child enduring trauma might have symptoms such as wanting to stay home from school, suffering tummy aches, problems sleeping or eating, bursts of anger, and many other kinds of attention-seeking behaviors.

Triggers and Trauma

✓ When trauma is triggered, we react out of proportion (most likely inappropriately) to the instigating event. As Menakem explains, "Whenever someone freaks out suddenly or reacts to a small problem as if it were a catastrophe, it's often a trauma response.

✓ Our trauma is triggered as a reaction to perceived danger.

✓ Trauma triggers happen far faster than our thinking minds can engage, leaving no time for the rational brain to evaluate whether or not the perceived threat is real.

✓ From the body's perspective, safety and danger are not cognitive concepts, they're visceral sensations. The body either feels safe, or it doesn't.

✓ When it feels unsafe, the body will do whatever is required to re-establish a sense of safety, triggering the flight-fight-freeze response.

Generational Trauma

✓ Trauma can be passed down generationally—where individuals don't remember present-life trauma.

✓ Trauma is transmitted to children through attachment relationships with parents who have experienced trauma, and this trauma can have an ongoing impact throughout their children's lives, including a predisposition to new or further trauma.

✓ Generational trauma can be at the root of anything from emotional numbness or hesitancies about discussing emotions to distrusting outsiders or exhibiting conflicting, aggressive behavior, or in anxious parents or caregivers who are overly protective of children and family members.

✓ Historically many oppressed or disenfranchised groups have been affected disproportionately by generational trauma, including black descendants of slaves, Native Americans, refugees, and descendants of Holocaust survivors just to name a few.

- ✓ For most black Americans, the accumulation of 400 years of racial oppression results in a significant depth of trauma.

- ✓ Slaves' experiences of being held against their will, followed by their descendants' experiences of being openly and systematically discriminated against, results in a profound and overwhelming lack of safety from one generation to the next.

Somatic Awareness of Trauma

- ✓ Somatic (in the body) work is useful to resolve issues that live in the mind *and* body as a result of traumatic events in our psychological past.

- ✓ Our bodies hold onto past trauma, and this trauma is then reflected in our body language, posture and expressions.

- ✓ When we successfully resolve the trauma in the body, the body no longer has a reason to overreact to situations that were previously threatening, allowing it to relax, breathe and restore itself to a sense of safety and resilience.

- ✓ Dr. Peter A. Levine, author of *Trauma and Memory* discovered that trauma is imprinted in our nervous systems not just in a fight or flight response, but also in a freeze response.

- ✓ Freeze happens when neither fight nor flight are options available in a stressful situation and the only option left is to freeze.

- ✓ For humans, when (for whatever reason) we can't go into fight or flight, that massive traumatic energy has nowhere to go, so it stays trapped within the body, keeping it on high alert.

- ✓ After that, this traumatic energy can trigger anytime we have feelings or bodily experiences similar to those that took place during the original trauma.

- ✓ Somatic trauma therapy techniques move and release this trapped energy so that it's not as easily activated in the future.

- ✓ Somatic techniques can also address trauma that goes way back in time—even preverbal trauma that occurred in infancy and generational trauma, or any trauma that was not imprinted by a present-life experience.

Perfectionism

✓ Perfectionism is much more difficult to resolve than other Impostor Behaviors because it's so often a response to trauma.

✓ The *thing* that lingers below the subconscious and triggers perfectionism is a deep-seated fear of unworthiness.

✓ The core belief that most perfectionists carry around with them is that they're loveable and worthy *only* when they are perfect.

✓ While perfectionism is often seen as a positive trait that gives us the energy to do our best, in reality it takes an enormous toll on our psyche and bodies.

✓ Perfectionism often arises from psychological wounds in childhood. Children who experience emotional trauma come to believe that they must prove their worthiness of love by being extremely competent and flawless.

✓ Perfectionism may also be passed down through generational trauma as a survival trait.

✓ Regardless of whether you descend from slaves or aristocrats, its purpose is to prevent you from experiencing painful circumstances that occurred generations ago.

TOOLS

The Body Scan

1. Think of a trigger you'd like to resolve.

2. Make a list of the feelings you experience when you are triggered. (*Example: angry, frustrated, powerless.*)

3. Take a few balancing breaths to relax your body and shift your awareness to your body with compassion and curiosity.

4. Slowly scan your body from your head downward and notice any sensations you may experience in your body that go along with the feelings you have when you're triggered. Note where you feel tightness, pain, tension or heaviness. As you slowly scan, notice the areas in your body where these sensations occur, and then describe the feeling as best you can. You might want to use words like sharp, tight, heavy, nauseous, chaotic, or whatever works for you. (*Example: I feel anxious; my neck and shoulders tense up. I feel my body getting warm, and I'm starting to sweat a little bit.*)

5. Just stay with those feelings and notice your breath going in and out of your lungs. Slow down and even out your breathing. Relax while you stay with that feeling and notice what happens in your body as you breathe. You might try resting your hands on your thighs and slowly tap your hands alternately on your right and left leg while you breathe. Try to match the pace of your tapping with your heartbeat.

6. As you do this, notice any thoughts, images or awareness that come to mind. (*Example: Along with this tightness in my chest, I notice I feel angry. And now I feel really sad. It's sad that I can't just be me, that I need to temper my energy and enthusiasm. It feels like I'm suffocating my spirit and all of my creative energy.*)

7. Keep breathing and see if there is a release. Does anything come to mind that speeds the relief? How does that make you feel? (*Example: I'm done with keeping myself bottled up. With that realization my lungs opened up. I feel that heavy weight lifting off my chest, and my throat loosen up. This feels so much lighter, better.*)

8. Stay with these new feelings in your body for a little longer while continuing to breathe.

9. As your breathing returns to normal, notice how any awareness you had might affect the situations in which you might be triggered in the future. (*Example: As an adult I don't need to be afraid of getting in trouble for my behavior like I did as a kid. I have good judgement now. I can decide how much of myself to unleash in any given situation.*)

10. Take three balancing breaths.

11. Butterfly tap for a few minutes to let the parts of you that know how to integrate the awareness, shifts and learnings.

WRITING EXERCISE

1. What childhood or earlier life experiences might have been traumatic for you?

_____

_____

_____

_____

_____

_____

_____

2. When you think of things that tend to be triggers for you, how might they relate to the traumatic events you recall from your childhood?

_____

_____

_____

_____

_____

_____

_____

3. For each of the traumatic experiences you can recall from your childhood, what decisions might the childhood version of you make in the moment when the trauma occurred? (Example: Jasmin decided that because she's black she would always be overlooked and never given a fair chance, thus would always have to fight for whatever she wants, because nobody else would fight for her.)

_____

_____

_____

_____

_____

_____

_____

_____

4. Thinking of your traumatic experiences as lenses through which you experience the world, what is a common experience that causes you stress, fear, anxiety? (Example: Jasmin's system is on high-alert for things that make her feel overlooked and not given a fair chance.)

_____

_____

_____

_____

_____

GUIDED WRITING EXERCISE

The Warm Cave Guided Exercise

1. Take three balancing breaths to relax your body and mind, slow your breathing, and reduce your heart rate.

2. Think of a circumstance in which your perfectionism kicks in.

3. Shift your awareness into your body with compassion and curiosity, and locate any uncomfortable physical feeling. Take a moment and focus on *where* in your body that feeling lives, and then once you find it, embrace *how* it feels. If it helps, you might even literally ask yourself, 'Where does this feeling live? And how does it feel in that place within me?' But don't pressure yourself, and don't rush. You don't need to articulate anything right now. Just sit with it, and *feel* it.

4. Notice what you discover, and what you feel. (*Example: I feel something in the center of my body, from my throat all the way down to my stomach. I'm surprised by how intense it is.*)

5. Keep breathing, and now cross your arms. Then slowly butterfly tap on each arm as we work through the feeling. Do this until you feel the sensation shift or release.

6. Now stop and observe the feelings in your body one part at a time. You might start by focusing on your throat and notice how that feels. Breathe and stay with that, and continue to focus your attention right there. And notice if anything changes.

7. When that feeling releases, you can move on to the next spot and repeat the process above. After you're done breathing, noticing and butterfly tapping, and when you feel some shifts or release, you can go to the next step.

8. Now imagine there's a super warm and cozy cave in your body, it could be in your chest or in your tummy. Whatever feels most comfortable.

9. Imagine what is in the cave that makes it particularly safe, comfortable and cozy for you. (*Example: There's a fire glowing inside, reflecting off the brown walls of the cave and casting a really warm glow. There's also a rug on the floor and a bunch of cozy, furry pillows, and blankets.*)

10. Imagine that you are going into the cave, and sit down in whatever spot in the cave that feels most comfortable and safe.

11. Now imagine someone very kind and very wise joining you in the cave. It could be an ancestor, or a person, or even an angel or a benevolent spirit. Perhaps it's a friend or a

parental figure, or maybe a fictional character in a movie. Notice if you can sense the presence of this kind and wise being. (*Example: It's my grandmother. I never met her because she passed away when I was two years old. But my mom always told me stories about her. She was so brilliant and courageous. She had such a bright and lively spirit. I feel her here with me.*)

12. Just be with whoever you imagine with you and sit silently and breathe. If you want, share your concerns about your perfectionism with this kind spirit do so. Then just allow that kind presence to be present and support you in whatever way is best.

13. Notice what you become aware of with regard to the wisdom, kindness and compassion that this wise spirit has with regard to your perfectionism. What does he or she say to you? What advice does he or she have for you?

14. Continue to breathe as you move that awareness through you, allowing you to integrate that wisdom into your system, all the way down to every cell.

15. Now in your mind float back into your childhood, imagining having this kind, wise spirit with you whenever you felt the feelings that drive your perfectionism. Just stay present with the memories and imagine the kind, compassionate presence of this wise spirit with you, there to help and protect you. Breathe and move your awareness back into your body like you did before. If it helps, picture this spirit comforting you. Perhaps she's holding you and gently rocking you. Whatever makes you feel safe and loved.

16. Notice what you feel, or thoughts that come into your mind as you just breathe and feel the wise spirit's presence and love.

17. Allow yourself to float backward in time even further, to any moment from the time you were born, or even before. Allow your wise spirit's love and warmth to be there for you no matter what you encounter. Feel your presence when you need her. Then float backward again..."

18. Now let's just grow you up slowly from that point. Float forward in time, with your wise spirit by your side, pausing briefly at every point along the way whenever you feel afraid, sad, or alone. Your wise spirit's love and presence will help you through that. And when you're all grown up, bring yourself back into the warm cave.

19. Notice how you feel now. What are the thoughts and feelings you have associated with those moments when you feel the need to be perfect now?

20. Now bring all of this awareness of your wise spirit's constant warmth and loving presence with you as you come out of the cave and back into the room with me. Allow this new awareness to integrate into your very cells, and take this experience with you in the days and weeks to come.

BodyFlow Series

Visit composurethebook.com/file to experience the Elevating Confidence & Accessing the Higher Authority BodyFlow video

It takes about 15 minutes. This BodyFlow video is a powerful tool designed to strengthen and integrate your powerful intention in your system so that you increase the likelihood of success.

CHAPTER 10

APPLYING EXECUTIVE PRESENCE

KEY TAKEAWAYS

Manager to Executive

✓ A first and critical inflection point in a career progression is the transition from a manager to a leader.

✓ Management consists of controlling a group of people to accomplish a goal. Leadership, however, is the ability to influence, motivate, and enable others outside of your management purview in order to contribute toward overall organizational success.

✓ What separates leaders from managers is how they use their influence to inspire, rather than how they wield power to control.

Power and Influence

✓ People decide how competent you are in 100 milliseconds.

✓ When it comes to projecting competence, 7% is attributed to your words, 35% to your presentation, and a whopping 55% to your body language.

✓ Body language communicates power and status and sets the stage for who leads in a situation.

✓ To be perceived as *authoritative*, all people (women *and* men) are expected to:

   ▷ Be expansive, take up maximum space.

   ▷ Speak in complete sentences.

   ▷ Hold eye contact when talking.

   ▷ Refrain from monitoring the responses of others.

✓ To be perceived as *approachable*, women are expected to:

   ▷ Maintain a tight, closed body.

   ▷ Speak cautiously.

   ▷ Avoid direct eye contact.

   ▷ Smile and nod in agreement.

✓ It's important for women to find the right balance between these opposing cues to match the situation.

✓ To maximize your influence, and the likelihood of achieving the outcome you desire, always position your requests in the context of the benefits they will bring the organization and those you're negotiating with.

Difficult Conversations

✓ It's important to pay attention to both the actual content and the delivery—which includes the emotional content—when engaging in difficult or high-stakes conversations.

✓ The "highest and best good" perspective is helpful to gain clarity on the right approach — paying attention to what is in the highest and best good of all parties (for example: you, the other party, your company, etc.).

✓ Most of us spend more than 95% of our time zeroed in on content and completely ignore the body language, energy, and emotions behind the delivery.

Active Listening

✓ Active listening is a key characteristic found in powerful, successful executives.

✓ Active listening involves being present and focused on what the other person is saying, listening with genuine curiosity, repeating back what you've heard in the same language the other person used, and asking questions to gain clarity and gather more information.

✓ To amplify your curiosity, ask "how" or "what" questions.

✓ Questions that spotlight *how* and *what* are more neutral than *why* questions, which tend to focus on opinions.

✓ "Why" questions can result in blame and judgement.

✓ "How" and "what" questions are a gift because of the clarity they provide for everyone involved.

The DJ Emotion Mixer

1. Imagine you're a DJ and that you have a mixer that you use to dial up and down various emotions (like a DJ would dial up and down base, treble, etc.).

2. Think of 3 to 5 traits that will be important in the discussion (for example: calm, curiosity, confidence).

3. Step through each emotion, one at a time, and experiment with dialing it up and down. Notice how that feels. If you have trouble dialing up an emotion, think of a time when you felt that emotion strongly, and load up that feeling in your system.

4. Decide what level you want to "dial" each emotion to the level you'd like to show up in the way you would like (on a scale of 1-10, 1 = low, 10 = high), and one by one move the dial to that emotional level, then feel the emotion at that level and breathe for a few seconds.

5. Move on to the next emotion and "add" that to the previous one, once dialing the emotion to the desired level, then feeling the emotion at that level and breathing for a few seconds.

6. Cycle through each emotion at the desired level to further integrate the combined emotional stance you desire.

7. Imagine yourself in the difficult or high-stakes conversation or situation that will benefit from this emotional state. Notice how you might react and respond in that situation with your emotions dialed into this new combined emotional state. Imagine how the other people might respond.

8. Make needed adjustments (if any) by going back through steps 4-7.

"How" and "What" Diet

Commit to a week of only asking "how" and "what" questions, even when others explicitly ask for advice or input. At the end of the week, reflect back on what was different as a result of asking only "how" and "what" questions.

Problem – Solution – Result (PSR)

The PSR format is an ideal format to communicate a problem to your manager or executive team. It not only identifies the problem, but also the proposed solution and expected outcomes and benefits.

1.   Think of a situation in which you need to communicate about a problem.

2.   State the problem concisely in two or three sentences.

3.   State a proposed solution to the problem concisely in a few sentences. Include any specific commitments you will make (what will you do by when) to increase your accountability and instill confidence in others that you have the problem under control.

4.   State the benefits and/or expected outcomes of the proposed solution.

Resourceful States

1. Think of a challenging situation for which you'd like to elevate your Executive Presence.

_____

_____

_____

_____

_____

2. Think of three to five emotions (for example: calm, confident, curious, courageous, powerful, charismatic, reactive, fearful, anxious, etc.) that you'd like to either amplify or diminish to be more resourceful in that situation.

_____

_____

_____

_____

_____

_____

_____

_____

3. For each emotional state, what is the ideal level of that emotion for the situation on a scale of 1 to 10 (1 = low, 10 = high) that would be most helpful for the situation.

_____

_____

_____

_____

_____

_____

_____

4. For each state, write down one or more examples of when you have experienced that emotional level.

_____

_____

_____

_____

_____

_____

_____

_____

5. Load up each emotion at the desired emotional level, one at a time, adding each emotional state to the previous. Now when you imagine yourself in the challenging situation in that ideal emotional state, what do you notice? How might the dynamics or outcome be different than if you were in a less resourceful state?

_____

_____

_____

_____

_____

_____

_____

_____

_____

_____

_____

_____

CHAPTER 11

THE JOY
FACTOR

———

KEY TAKEAWAYS

✓ When you factor the *whole* you into your life, your priorities change.

✓ As you become more aligned with your true self and core values, your emotional energy elevates to a higher good. As a result, you will be guided and supported in unexpected ways.

✓ Peak performance occurs when individuals function at optimal levels, also known as being in the zone or in a state of flow. This happens when we operate with a combination of positive emotions and high energy.

✓ The underlying theory behind states of consciousness is that thought patterns generate energy, which vibrate at various frequencies. The higher the emotional state, the higher the frequency.

✓ One way to take personal responsibility and ownership of your own energy and emotions in your life and your work is to complete the following sentences, listing as many things as you can come up with:

> ▷ I turn myself off when ...

> ▷ I turn myself on when ...

The Joy Gap

✓ People intrinsically seek joy, and joy connects everyone more powerfully than almost any other human experience.

✓ 90% of workers expect to experience joy at work, but only 37% report actually feeling joy, leaving a joy gap of 53%.

The Flow Scale

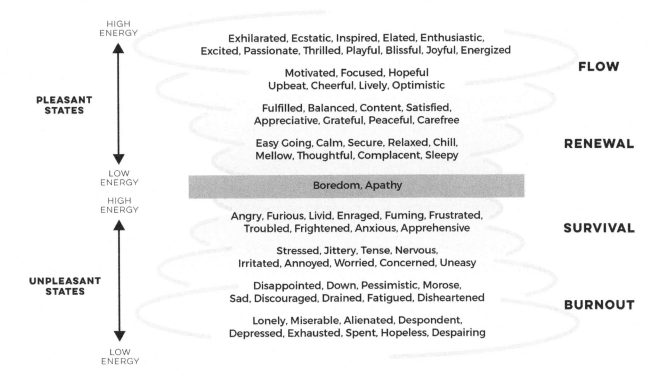

✓ The flow scale can be used to understand your current energetic and emotional state, and provide you with insights into how to get into a more positive, productive state.

    ▷ Pleasant emotional states are in the top half, while unpleasant emotional states are in the bottom half.

    ▷ The state of FLOW, a high-performance and highly creative state, exists when energy is high and the emotional state is pleasant.

    ▷ The state of RENEWAL, a productive and relaxed state where energy is conserved and replenished, results from the combination of pleasant emotional states with lower energy.

    ▷ The SURVIVAL state, which often results when we're triggered, occurs when we experience unpleasant emotions combined with high energy.

    ▷ The state of BURNOUT often occurs after a SURVIVAL state when triggered energy subsides but our unpleasant emotions persist.

TOOLS

Managing Up – Weekly Reporting Template

This format streamlines and provides effective reporting. Our template has three sections, no more than three items per section, and no more than two or three sentences per item. The three top-level sections are as follows:

1. Breakthroughs – something significant that happened during the week, and as a result it cleared a roadblock or made something possible.

2. Challenges or Risks with the Mitigation Strategy (be sure to include next steps and timeline).

3. Requests or Input – things you would like from your manager or executive team to help you resolve challenges or risks.

Reflections

Reflect on the past days and weeks since you started reading the book and completing this workbook:

1. Make a list of as many things as you can think of that have shifted to be more positive. (Example: *I am speaking up more in meetings, I notice that I'm less sensitive when I receive criticism.*)

_____

_____

_____

_____

_____

_____

_____

_____

_____

_____

_____

_____

2. Make a list of as many examples in which you've used tools from the book. Have these tools made you more composed and effective?

_____

_____

_____

_____

_____

_____

_____

_____

_____

_____

_____

_____

_____

_____

_____

_____

3. In what ways have you become more aware of your own interests and passions, and what you value and stand for? How has this awareness changed your experiences in your work and your life?

_____

_____

_____

_____

_____

_____

4. In what ways would you like your life to be more fulfilling, more aligned with things that are more meaningful and better purpose?

_____

_____

_____

_____

_____

_____

5. List as many examples as you can recall of ways you have experienced positive
serendipity or unexpected ease.

Evaluating your Work on the Flow Scale

1. For several days keep a list of the things you do every day, bucketing similar tasks (such as meetings, email, and writing status reports).

_____

_____

_____

_____

_____

_____

_____

_____

_____

_____

_____

_____

_____

2. Estimate the percentage of time you spend in each of these buckets.

_____

_____

_____

_____

_____

_____

3. For each type of work:

     a. Using the Flow Scale, identify the emotional states associated with the work.

     b. Does this category of work bring you close enough to joy?

_____

_____

_____

_____

_____

_____

_____

_____

c. If not, what emotional state would you like to experience? Brainstorm ideas about what might you do to elevate the tasks to result in a state that is closer to joy.

_____

_____

_____

_____

_____

_____

_____

d. For those tasks that rank low on the Joy scale, what might you delegate or even stop doing?

_____

_____

_____

_____

_____

_____

4. In your work, freewrite answers to the following statements, making a list of as many things you can think of that turn you on, and turn you off:

a. I turn myself off when ...

_____

_____

_____

_____

_____

_____

b. I turn myself on when ...

_____

_____

_____

_____

_____

_____

GUIDED WRITING EXERCISE

Letter from Your 70 Year Old Self

1. Choose a time when you have at least 30 minutes where you will be uninterrupted.

2. Take three balancing breaths to calm and center yourself.

3. **Visit composurethebook.com/file to listen to the guided meditation for the exercise.**

4. Describe yourself at seventy. What did you do after fifty that you enjoyed? Be very specific. Now, write a letter from you at seventy to you at your current age. What would you tell yourself? What interests would you urge yourself to pursue? What dreams would you encourage?

_____

_____

_____

_____

_____

_____

_____

_____

_____

_____

_____

_____

CHAPTER 12
ENVISION

KEY TAKEAWAYS

✓ Cultivating vision can be taught and learned, just like any desired skill.

✓ For leaders, vision ranks a close second after honesty as the most important trait. In contrast, only 27% of people look for vision in colleagues.

✓ Vision is what distinguishes leaders from managers and individual contributors.

✓ Visionaries are rare. According to Myers-Briggs, natural visionaries represent less than 5% of the population.

✓ Vision is important because it creates a perspective of a desired future in the present. This perspective can help guide you when you're at an important crossroad in your work and life.

Above the Clouds Meditation

1. Choose a time when you have at least 30 minutes where you will be uninterrupted.

2. Take three balancing breaths to calm and center yourself.

3. **Visit composurethebook.com/file to listen to the guided meditation for the exercise**

4. Freewrite for 10 minutes about your experiences, ah-has, and inspirations you received from your journey above the clouds.

_____

_____

_____

_____

_____

_____

_____

_____

_____

_____

_____

ENVISION

BodyFlow Series

Visit composurethebook.com/file to experience the Taking your Vision Forward BodyFlow video

It takes about 15 minutes. This BodyFlow video is a powerful tool designed to strengthen and integrate your powerful intention in your system so that you increase the likelihood of success.

Made in the USA
Monee, IL
12 October 2021